Cooking up Memories

from you to me®

from you to me®

concept by Neil Coxon

Cooking up Memories

from you to me®

This book is for the favourite recipes and food anecdotes of your family or friends.

It is to capture some of those wonderful dishes or drinks that they have made for you and others over the years.

Ask them to complete it carefully and, if they want to, add some photographs or images to personalise it more.

When it is finished and returned to you, this will be a record of an amazing collection of recipes and stories that you will treasure forever.

Dear

Here is a gift from me to you . . . for you to give to me.

Food can produce powerful memories and I can clearly remember some of the lovely things you have made over the years.

Please can you capture some of them in here along with your answers to my questions about your life with food and then give the book back to me.

I have listed some of the things you have made and I would really like the recipe for these as well as for other favourites you like making.

People say that we all have at least one book in us, and this will be one of yours.

The story of some of our favourite food that I will treasure forever.

Thank you,

"After a good dinner, one can forgive anybody, even one's own relatives."

Oscar Wilde

These are some of the wonderful things
I remember you making. Please will you include the
recipe for these within this collection as well as
others you think I will like . . .

Tell me the story of how you learned to cook...

What were some of your favourite childhood foods?

What were the **first dishes** you remember making?

Sweet shops bring back great memories . . .
what would be some of your favourite sweets?

How has the food you eat changed throughout your lifetime?

What are some of the most unusual foods or drinks you have ever tasted?

What family traditions about food or meals can you tell me about?

Tell me some **fond memories** you have of family meals . . .

Describe what would make up your favourite
meal...

What are your favourite drinks?

Describe your **most memorable** meal or meals . . .

Tell me about the **best restaurants** you have experienced . . .

Who has influenced you most with regard to food and cooking?

Tell me about your **most disasterous** cooking experience . . .

If you could invite anyone, living or dead, to your dinner party, who would they be?

Describe your 'perfect day' when it comes to food . . . where would you have breakfast, what would you eat, what would you do for lunch?

What other **anecdotes** and **stories** can you tell me about your life with food?

When it comes to food, what would you like us to do together?

Favourite Recipes

Recipe name

Tell me the story behind this recipe . . .

Ingredients

Method

Recipe name

Tell me the story behind this recipe . . .

Ingredients

Method

Recipe name

Tell me the story behind this recipe . . .

Ingredients

Method

Recipe name

Tell me the story behind this recipe . . .

Ingredients

Method

Recipe name

Tell me the story behind this recipe . . .

Ingredients

Method

Recipe name

Tell me the story behind this recipe . . .

Ingredients

Method

Recipe name

Tell me the story behind this recipe . .,.

Ingredients

Method

Recipe name

Tell me the story behind this recipe . . .

Ingredients

Method

Recipe name

Tell me the story behind this recipe . . .

Ingredients

Method

Recipe name

Tell me the story behind this recipe . . .

Ingredients

Method

Recipe name

Tell me the story behind this recipe . . .

Ingredients

Method

Recipe name

Tell me the story behind this recipe . . .

Ingredients

Method

Recipe name

Tell me the story behind this recipe . . .

Ingredients

Method

Recipe name

Tell me the story behind this recipe . . .

Ingredients

Method

Recipe name

Tell me the story behind this recipe . . .

Ingredients

Method

Recipe name

Tell me the story behind this recipe . . .

Ingredients

Method

Recipe name

Tell me the story behind this recipe . . .

Ingredients

Method

Recipe name

Tell me the story behind this recipe . . .

Ingredients

Method

Recipe name

Tell me the story behind this recipe . . .

Ingredients

Method

Recipe name

Tell me the story behind this recipe . . .

Ingredients

Method

Recipe name

Tell me the story behind this recipe . . .

Ingredients

Method

Recipe name

Tell me the story behind this recipe . . .

Ingredients

Method

Recipe name

Tell me the story behind this recipe . . .

Ingredients

Method

Recipe name

Tell me the story behind this recipe . . .

Ingredients

Method

Recipe name

Tell me the story behind this recipe . . .

Ingredients

Method

Recipe name

Tell me the story behind this recipe . . .

Ingredients

Method

Recipe name

Tell me the story behind this recipe . . .

Ingredients

Method

Recipe name

Tell me the story behind this recipe . . .

Ingredients

Method

Recipe name

Tell me the story behind this recipe . . .

Ingredients

Method

Recipe name

Tell me the story behind this recipe . . .

Ingredients

Method

Volume conversions

In most of the world, recipes use the metric system of litres and millilitres, grams and kilograms, and degrees Celsius.

The English speaking world frequently measures weight in pounds, with volume measures based on cooking utensils and pre-metric measures. The actual values are often different from the utensils on which they were based and there is little consistency from one country to another.

Measure	UK	Australia	USA
Teaspoon	5 ml	5 ml	4.93 ml
Dessertspoon	10 ml	–	–
Tablespoon	15 ml	20 ml	14.79 ml
Cup	285 ml	250 ml	236.59 ml
fl oz	28.41 ml	28.41 ml	29.57 ml
Pint	568.26 ml	568.26 ml	473.18 ml
Quart	1136.52 ml	1136.52 ml	946.35 ml
Gallon	4546.09 ml	4546.09 ml	3785.41 ml

Volume conversions

fluid ounces / pints	millilitres
1 fl oz	30 ml
2 fl oz	60 ml
3 fl oz	90 ml
5 fl oz (¼ pint)	150 ml
10 fl oz (½ pint)	290 ml
15 fl oz (¾ pint)	440 ml
1 pint	590 ml
1¼ pints	740 ml
1¾ pints	1 litre
2 pints	1.2 litres
2½ pints	1.5 litres
4 pints	2.4 litres

Measurement conversions

inches	millimetre / centimetres
⅛ inch	3 mm
¼ inch	5 mm
½ inch	1 cm
¾ inch	2 cm
1 inch	2.5 cm
1¼ inches	3 cm
1½ inches	4 cm
1¾ inches	4.5 cm
2 inches	5 cm
2½ inches	6 cm
3 inches	7.5 cm
3½ inches	9 cm
4 inches	10 cm

Measurement conversions

inches	millimetre / centimetres
5 inches	13 cm
5¼ inches	13.5 cm
6 inches	15 cm
6½ inches	16 cm
7 inches	18 cm
7½ inches	19 cm
8 inches	20 cm
9 inches	23 cm
9½ inches	24 cm
10 inches	25 cm
11 inches	28 cm
12 inches	30 cm

To be exact: 1 inch = 25.4 mm

Weight conversions

ounces / pounds	grams / kilograms
½ oz	10 g
¾ oz	20 g
1 oz	25 g
1½ oz	40 g
2 oz	50 g
2½ oz	60 g
3 oz	75 g
4 oz	110 g
4½ oz	125 g
5 oz	150 g
6 oz	175g

Weight conversions

ounces / pounds	grams / kilograms
7 oz	200 g
8 oz	225 g
9 oz	250 g
10 oz	275 g
12 oz	350 g
1 lb	450 g
1½ lb	700 g
2 lb	900 g
3 lb	1.3 kg
5 lb	2 kg

To be exact: 1 oz = 28.3495 g

Cooking temperature conversions

Gas Mark	Fahrenheit	Centigrade	Aga Setting
¼	225°F	110°C	Very Cool
½	250°F	120°C	Very Cool
1	275°F	135°C	Very Cool
2	300°F	150°C	Cool
3	325°F	165°C	Warm
4	350°F	180°C	Warm
5	375°F	190°C	Medium
6	400°F	200°C	Medium / High
7	425°F	220°C	Medium / High
8	450°F	230°C	High
9	475°F	250°C	Very High

For fan ovens, reduce recipe temperature by 20°

To be exact: $°C = (°F - 32) \times \tfrac{5}{9}$ and $°F = (°C \times \tfrac{9}{5}) + 32$

Eggs

Description	Weight	Size
XL Very Large	73 g & over	0, 1
L Large	63 g to 72 g	1, 2, 3
M Medium	53 g to 62 g	3, 4, 5
S Small	under 53 g	5, 6, 7

Eggs are a perishable food and fresh eggs in their shell will keep for around 3 to 4 weeks.

Hard boiled eggs will last around 1 week.

To see how old an uncooked egg is, drop it gently into a bowl of cold water.
If it:

- sinks to the bottom and stays there, it is about 3 to 6 days old

- sinks but floats at an angle, it's more than a week old

- sinks, but stands on end, it is about two weeks old

- floats, it is too old and should be discarded

These extra pages are for us to write any food

questions, memories or answers that

may not have been covered elsewhere in the journal . . .

And finally for the record . . .

what is your full name ?

what is your date of birth ?

what was the date when you completed this journal for me ?

Dear

I will treasure this book, your recipes and your memories forever.

I hope you enjoyed completing this book and answering my questions.

Thank you so much for doing it and for writing your own book about you and your food . . .

from you to me

Cooking up Memories
from you to me®

Mixed Sources
Product group from well-managed
forests and other controlled sources
www.fsc.org Cert no. TT-COC-2082
© 1996 Forest Stewardship Council
FSC

This paper is manufactured from material sourced from forests certified according to strict environmental, social and economical standards.

If you liked the concept of this book, please tell your family and friends and look out for others in the *from you to me* range:

Dear Mum, from you to me
Dear Dad, from you to me
Dear Grandma, from you to me
Dear Grandad, from you to me
Dear Sister, from you to me
Dear Brother, from you to me
Dear Friend, from you to me
other relationships and memory journals coming soon . . .